> # Christmas Carols & Prayers

By Mary Erickson
Illustrated by Don Page

Journey to Bethlehem

Thank you, God, for the

that carried  on its back.

Thank you for  who led them

over hills and a long winding

Thank you for shade where

rested and for green grass the

nibbled. Thank you for the in

the sky that lit the way. Thank you, God,

for taking them safely to the

of Bethlehem.

Hark! the Herald Angels Sing

Hark! the herald   sing,

"Glory to the newborn   ;

Peace on   , and mercy mild,

God and sinners reconciled!"

Joyful, all ye nations, rise,

Join the triumph of the skies;

With the angelic host proclaim,

"Christ is born in Bethlehem!"

—*Charles Wesley*

Christmas Joys

Thanks for my ____ that hear

ringing and carols the ____ is

singing. Thanks for my ____ that see

burning and Christmas ____ twinkling.

Thanks for my nose that smells

baking and ____ roasting.

Thanks for my ⬚ that tastes peppermint and hot ⬚ cider. Thanks for my ⬚ that feels happy when I worship the 👶 in the ⬚.

Thank you, God, for the joys of Christmas.

The Angels' Song

Dear God, I wish I'd been a   watching

on the night when your

appeared in the night sky. I wish I'd heard the

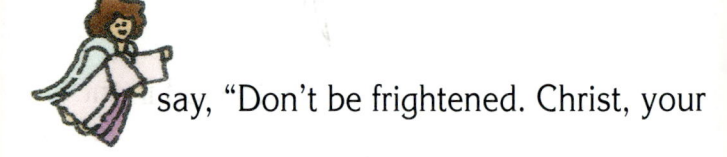

say, "Don't be frightened. Christ, your

Savior, is born in the   of Bethlehem

tonight. Go! You'll find   Jesus

wrapped in soft white cloth and lying in

a 🔲 in a 🏠." I wish I'd seen

the sky full of

and heard them sing, "Glory to God in the

highest and peace to everywhere."

In the Bleak Midwinter

What can I give him, poor as I am?

If I were a

I would bring a   ;

If I were a

I would do my part;

Yet what can I give him—

Give my   .

—*Christina Rossetti*

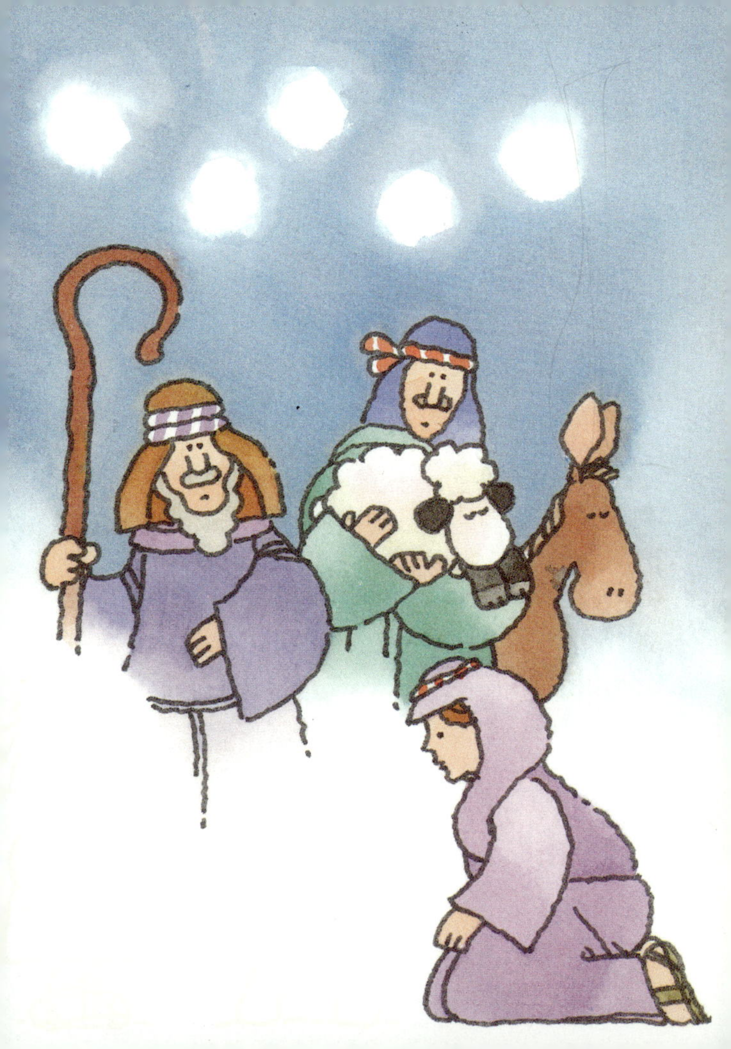

What Can I Do for Jesus?

Dear Father in heaven, thanks for the

that carried Mary to Bethlehem,

and for the　　　　　　who obeyed your

. Thanks for the　　　that shared

and　　　　, and for the

who followed your   . Like the   ,

I can be useful. Like the   ,

I can quickly obey. Like the   ,

I can share with others. Like the   ,

I will worship Jesus today.

Christmas Decorations

Thank you, God, for our Christmas

with shiny   and twinkling

Thank you for   with tall flames

brightening the night through our

Thank you for the   standing

on our table, playing   and   ,

singing a Christmas carol. Thank you for the

holly   hanging on the   ,

cheering passing   and welcoming

our friends.

Once in Royal David's City

Once in royal David's   , stood a

lonely cattle shed, where a mother laid her

          in a   for his   .

Mary was that mother mild, Jesus Christ

her little   .

He came down to earth from heaven, who is God and Lord of all, and his shelter was a stable, and his cradle was a stall. With the poor and mean and lowly, lived on earth our Savior holy.

—*Anonymous*

Remembering Jesus' Birthday

Dear Jesus, when   and   think

about Christmas, they might think of

in a   pulled by   , or

an   in a green pointed

making   in toyland. They might

think of a   with   and

, and a   , like a   or

, under the   . But I'll

remember how   worshiped the

in the   . And I'll sing,

"Happy birthday, dear Jesus."

Baking Cookies

Dear God, thank you for my family and the

fun we have when we mix   ,   ,

and   in a   . Thank you for

the way we laugh when we pat the dough and

roll it flat with a   . Thank you for

our cookie   that shape the

dough into a ⭐ or 🎄 or candy

🍭. When the baking is over, we pack

some 🍪 in a box. We knock on our

neighbors' door and give them the 🎁.

Thank you for the fun and joy of giving.

Away in a Manger

Away in a   , no   for a

          , the little Lord Jesus laid down

his sweet   ; The   in

the sky looked down where he lay, the

little Lord Jesus, asleep on the

The   are lowing, the

awakes, but little Lord Jesus no crying he

makes; I love thee, Lord Jesus! Look down

from the sky, and stay by my   ,

till morning is nigh.

—*John McFarland*

We Three Kings

We three [kings] of Orient are; bearing [gifts], we traverse afar, and [field] fountain, moor and [mountain], following yonder [star]. O [star] of wonder, [star] of night, [star] with royal beauty bright, westward leading, still proceeding, guide us to thy perfect light.

—J.H. Hopkins, Jr.